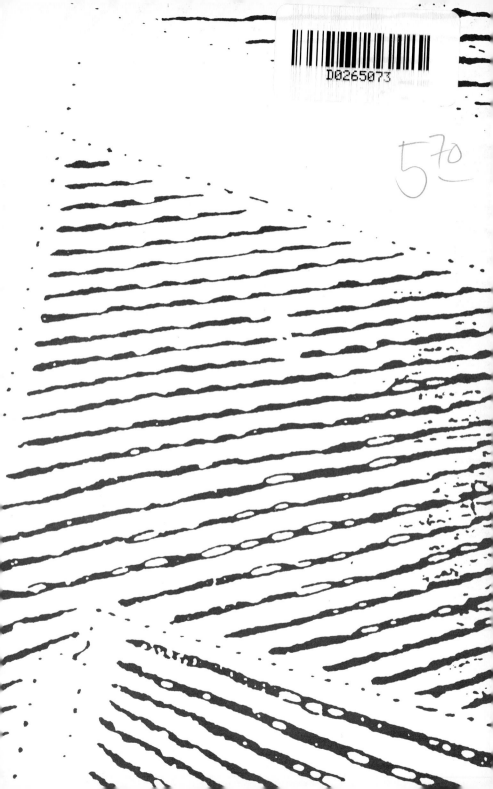

570

The Collected BLURTINGS of BAXTER

IT WAS HARVEY'S BOLD PLAN TO ARRIVE
AT THE ENEMY HEADQUARTERS AT
PORT ARTHUR UNDETECTED

LITTLE, BROWN AND COMPANY
Boston · New York · Toronto · London

First Edition

ISBN 0-316-90542-9

A CIP catalogue record for this book is available from the British Library.

Designed by David Fordham

Published simultaneously in Great Britain by Little, Brown and Company (UK) Ltd, and in
Canada by Little, Brown & Company (Canada) Limited

PRINTED AND BOUND IN ITALY

The majority of the images reproduced in this book are available as greetings cards, posters
and postcards from Santoro Graphics, 63 Maltings Place, Bagley's Lane, London SW6 2BY.

GLEN BAXTER

A PREFACE

I FIRST CAME ACROSS THE WORK OF GLEN BAXTER AT THE ANNUAL Festival of Yodelling in Ghent in 1957. It was on the third day of a particularly heated seminar that a young Belgian painter stepped forward brandishing what appeared at first sight to be a tattered piece of vellum, its surface covered with a series of scratchy, wavering lines that could only indicate the presence of a fevered mind. At this juncture, a uniformed steward stepped up and demanded the removal of both the Belgian and the mysterious yellow oblong. A scuffle broke out and I heard someone cry, 'It's a Baxter!' To roars of disbelief, an ugly mob surged out of the shadows and across the great hall. Luckily I had the presence of mind to drop to my knees and send a wickerwork chair skittering straight into their path. I leapt over the bewildered steward, snatched the parchment from the Belgian's hand, made it to the side door and dashed into the street where I managed to hail a taxi.

Some three hours later I was sitting in the study of Mr van Kooten, the eminent art historian. I handed him the cream-coloured paper with its fascinating, if somewhat incoherent marks and scratches, and it was then that he uttered his now famous pronouncement: 'It's worthless!'

Since that time, of course, Baxter's work has gone on to reach a worldwide audience, and Mr van Kooten is now President of the Ghent Academy of Plastic Arts. During a recent television interview, Mr van Kooten was handed a copy of this book. He looked at it very carefully for a few moments, then closed his eyes, and pressing together the fingers of both hands, he announced, 'This is rather like something I first saw in 1957.'

WILMA DE BIE
BELIZE, MAY 1993

BLURTINGS *about*
BAXTER

'Lucid, brilliant and quixotic, Baxter's works explore timeless issues of desire and mortality.'

BRUCE HOLVIG, *South Pudsey Literary Review*

'Glen Baxter's drawings are, without doubt, amongst some of the most appalling I have ever seen.'

ANDREW HITCHINSON, *The Gosport Daily Bugle*

'Who is Baxter, what is he? The sum, obviously, of everything. Yet with an individual magic glow. His genius is the depiction of "reality" both as text and as what it seems, beyond deconstruction, to be, or threatens to become, which is the subject.'

ELIOT FREMONT SMITH, *Village Voice*

'The vertiginous proximity of the erotic underpins the central thrust of his work.'

KERSLEY RHOADES, *The Oakland Pottery Review*

'L'absurde ainsi déclenché provoque le rire, la stupeur, voire l'incompréhension, selon que l'on goûte ou non les non-sens de ce maître de l'humour anglais.'

SYLVIA JUMERT, *La Croix*

More BLURTINGS *about* BAXTER

'Glen Baxter is an artist in the distinguished tradition of Lewis Carroll, Sax Rohmer, Marquis de Sade, Raymond Roussel, Luther Burbank and the Comte de Lautréamont. Welcome to the works.'

JOHN ASHBERY, *The New York Times*

'Een gediplomeerd accountant uit Zagreb die onder een halfgekookt exemplaar van *Wuthering Heights* in slaap pleegt te vallen. Glen Baxter is een Engelse tekenaar.'

PETER NIJMEIJER, *The Tulip Monthly*

'Samuel Beckett meets Tom Mix.'

MARY BLUME, *International Herald Tribune*

'Mr Baxter betrays all the ominous symptoms of genius.' EDWARD GOREY, *Cape Cod Gazette*

'Glen Baxter est le prince du nonsens.'

FELIX KOHN, *Libération*

'Baxter – he's an original, absolutely. There's nobody quite like him. Either in subject matter or in peculiar angle of vision on reality – or unreality, whatever the case.' WILLIAM KENNEDY, *The Washington Times*

HOW HE HATED SATURDAY
MORNING SHOPPING

IT WAS OUR FIRST DATE AND ALREADY I WAS BEGINNING TO HARBOUR SERIOUS RESERVATIONS ABOUT OUR FUTURE TOGETHER

I NEVER FULLY RECOVERED FROM THE APPALLING SHOCK OF DISCOVERING MY FATHER'S COLLECTION OF FLEETWOOD MAC ALBUMS...

UNCLE FRANK WOULD KEEP US
AMUSED FOR HOURS

BIG AL'S TULIP THRESHOLD
WAS NOTORIOUSLY LOW

I KNEW THERE WAS SOMETHING
SLIGHTLY DISCONCERTING ABOUT
JULIAN, BUT HIS CAREER
PROSPECTS WERE EXCELLENT

FELICITY HAD RESERVED A SOMEWHAT
LESS THAN LUKEWARM RECEPTION
FOR HER SOCIAL WORKER

THE ATMOSPHERE AT Nº 246 WAS
BECOMING INCREASINGLY TENSE

I LIVED IN CONSTANT FEAR OF AN OUTBREAK OF YODELLING

THERE, AS USUAL, WAS EDELSON, DELIVERING
HIS POST-STRUCTURALIST ANALYSIS OF THE
MODERN NOVEL TO THE PRIVILEGED FEW

WE DECIDED NOT TO INTERRUPT HIM
WHILST HE WAS ENGAGED IN SUCH
COMPLEX CALCULATIONS

I HAD OFTEN WONDERED ABOUT
THE TOTAL ABSENCE OF WILDLIFE
AT BIDDINGTON MANOR

AS A FIRST SEXUAL EXPERIENCE IT
HAD NOT BEEN A TOTAL DISAPPOINTMENT

"I CAN'T BE ABSOLUTELY CERTAIN, OF COURSE, BUT YOU DO APPEAR TO BE IN SOME KIND OF TROUBLE, MR. HOWARD"

FOR YEARS MURIEL HAD SEARCHED FOR MR. RIGHT; A MAN OF WIT, INTELLIGENCE AND SENSITIVITY, IN COMMAND OF HIS DESTINY. SHE FOUND EUGENE.

ERIC WAS NOW BEGINNING TO WISH HE'D
RETURNED HIS OVERDUE LIBRARY BOOKS

AS HE REACHED THE FINAL PARAGRAPH OF HIS MARRIAGE PROPOSAL, BILLY NOTICED THAT RUTH WAS NO LONGER THERE

ASKING SIMON TO LEND A HAND
IN THE KITCHEN WAS ALWAYS
A BIG MISTAKE...

TODAY WAS INDEED SPECIAL. UNCLE EDGAR
USUALLY ONLY COATED HIS LEFT LEG IN
MAYONNAISE WHILST WHISTLING THE
THEME MUSIC FROM "DR. ZHIVAGO"

ALISON WAS OUT THERE AGAIN
GLOWERING AT MY TASSEL

IT WAS THE ONE MOMENT OF THE DAY
THAT MISS CHAMBLEY HAD COME TO DREAD

IT WAS DURING A BRISK GAME
OF PING-PONG THAT I BEGAN TO
REALIZE THAT BRENDA'S FEELINGS
TOWARD ME HAD SOMEHOW CHANGED

IT PROVED TO BE THE END OF
A BEAUTIFUL RELATIONSHIP

LOUIS MANAGED TO TURN EVERY MEAL INTO A SPECIAL OCCASION

"HAS EITHER OF YOU TWO SEEN MY COLLECTION OF NEIL SEDAKA ALBUMS?" QUERIED THE RECTOR

HE SEEMED TO THINK I HAD
NEVER SWEPT A FLOOR BEFORE

FATHER SEEMED TO HAVE A
SLIGHT DANDRUFF PROBLEM

HE TOOK HER IN HIS ARMS AND
GENTLY SQUEEZED HER GOATEE

VANCE LIVED IN CONSTANT FEAR
OF LOSING HIS WRISTWATCH

A WIND OF CHANGE WAS SWEEPING THROUGH THE OLD BUNKHOUSE AND ZEKE DIDN'T CARE FOR IT ONE LITTLE BIT

IT WAS THE SMALLEST PIZZA
THEY HAD EVER SEEN

AS THE EVENING WORE ON I BEGAN
TO SUSPECT THAT I WAS IN THE
PRESENCE OF A DESPERATE MAN

"THIS IS WHERE I KEEP MY CHEWING GUM, YOUNG LAD" HE CONFIDED.